Sophie & The Spanish Magician

At The Fair

One day Sophie went to a fair with her parents and they saw a Spanish magician.

Hola,

Me llamo Lucas.

The magician greeted everyone with **Hola**. This means hello in Spanish.

Then he said in Spanish that his name was Lucas.

For his first trick, the Spanish magician put three boxes on a table. He placed a coin in one of the boxes and then told everyone to clap and count to three in Spanish.

uno   dos   tres

(Now the magician needs as much help as possible, so if you're reading this story now, please join in too!)

Then they all had to guess which box the coin was in!

Sophie watched in amazement. It wasn't in **uno**.
It wasn't in **dos**. And it *wasn't* in **tres**!

The coin had disappeared!

For his next trick, he asked everyone to clap and say three times **un conejo**.

un conejo   un conejo

U N   C O N E J O

Sophie's mum whispered to her that **un conejo** was the Spanish way of saying a rabbit.

And then suddenly out of his hat came…….

un conejo

Next the Spanish magician got out his wand.

He told everyone to clap and say three times **un pájaro**.

un pájaro   un pájaro

UN PÁJARO

Sophie's mum whispered to her that **un pájaro** was the Spanish word for a bird.

Suddenly **un pájaro** appeared on the table!

How had he done that? It was amazing!

Next he turned to Sophie and he asked:

¿Cuál es tu animal preferido?

un perro

Sophie realised that **animal preferido** meant favourite animal. So she replied **un perro** as her favourite animal was a dog. Surely he couldn't make **un perro** appear!

This time he had a very long balloon in his hand. He asked the crowd to join in with him as he said

" un perro   un perro   U N P E R R O "

And then suddenly the balloon turned into....

un perro

It had been so much fun watching the Spanish magician! For his final trick he placed his hat on the floor and he asked everyone to say **caramelos** three times as they clapped:

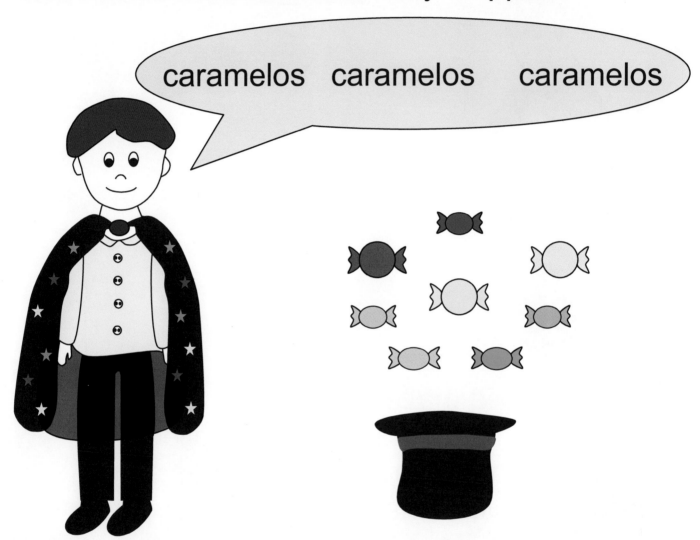

caramelos   caramelos   caramelos

And out of the hat came **unos caramelos** - lots and lots of delicious looking sweets! That was really amazing! Everyone thanked the Spanish magician by saying "**Gracias.**".

That was the Spanish magician's last trick, so they all said "**Adiós**". That means goodbye in Spanish.

Sophie & The Spanish Magician

Sophie's Birthday Party

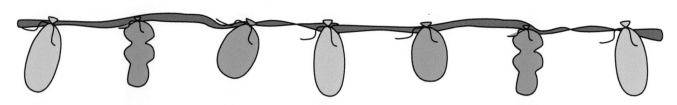

It was Sophie's birthday, and the Spanish magician arrived at her birthday party!

Hola,
Me llamo Lucas.

The Spanish magician said hello in Spanish. Then he said that his name was Lucas.

Hola,
Me llamo Sophie.

Sophie introduced herself in Spanish to the Spanish magician.

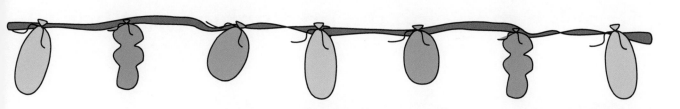

The Spanish magician asked
Sophie how she was:

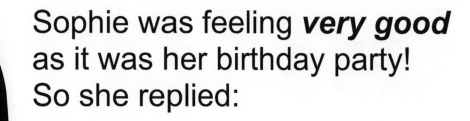

¿Cómo estás?

Sophie was feeling **very good**
as it was her birthday party!
So she replied:

Muy bien.

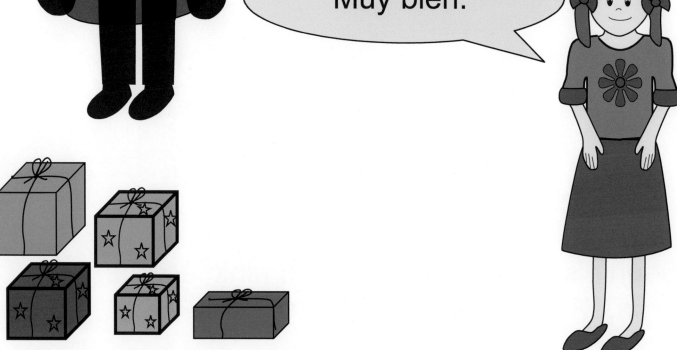

The Spanish magician asked Sophie what her favourite colour was.

Sophie's favourite colour was pink, so she said **rosa**. **Rosa** is pink in Spanish.

Okay, boys and girls I need your help!
We need to say **rosa** three times as we clap.

(Now the magician needs as much help as possible, so if you're reading this story now, please join in too!)

rosa   rosa   rosa

And out of the hat came a teddy that was the colour….

rosa

Sophie was so happy that she thanked the magician in Spanish.

Next the magician turned to Sophie's best friend, and he asked:

Sophie's best friend said blue was her favourite colour.

Okay, boys and girls I need your help!
We need to say **azul** three times as we clap.

(Now the magician needs as much help as possible, so if you're reading this story now, please join in too!)

azul   azul   azul

And out of the hat came a teddy that was the colour….

azul

Sophie's best friend was so happy that she thanked the magician in Spanish.

Next the Spanish magician asked a little boy:

The little boy said green was his favourite colour.

Okay, boys and girls I need your help!
We need to say **verde** three times as we clap.

(Now the magician needs as much help as possible, so if you're reading this story now, please join in too!)

verde   verde   verde

And out of the hat came a teddy that was the colour....

verde

Wow, what a magician!

Out of the hat kept on coming more and more teddies for Sophie's friends!

lila

amarillo

rojo

naranja

Eventually EVERYONE had a new teddy!

Can you remember the colours in Spanish for all the new teddies?   Lets say them together!

rojo

naranja

verde

lila

azul

rosa

amarillo

It had been a wonderful birthday party! The magician waved goodbye and they all said "Adiós."

Useful Spanish words and phrases

Hola ………………………………… Hello

Me llamo Lucas………………….… My name is Lucas

¿Cómo estás?………………….... How are you?

Muy bien …………………………... Very well

Gracias…………………………….… Thank you

Adiós………….………………….... Goodbye

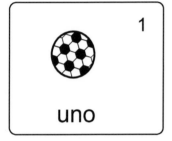
1
uno

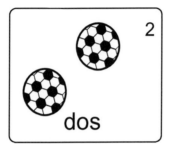
2
dos

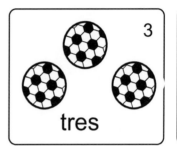
3
tres

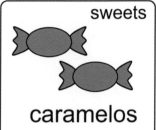
sweets
caramelos

¿Cuál es tu animal preferido?..... What is your favourite animal?

a rabbit
un conejo

a bird
un pájaro

a dog
un perro

¿Cuál es tu color preferido?……. What is your favourite colour?

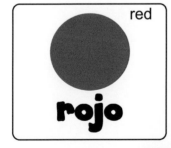
red
rojo

orange
naranja

yellow
amarillo

green
verde

blue
azul

lilac
lila

pink
rosa

Let's sing a song!

The following words could either be sung to a made up tune, or you could try saying the words as a rap.

For inspiration of a melody to use you could hum first a nursery rhyme. How many different versions can you create using the lyrics?

rojo naranja, rojo naranja
verde azul, verde azul
rosa lila, rosa lila
amarillo, amarillo

rojo naranja, rojo naranja
verde azul, verde azul
rosa lila, rosa lila
amarillo, amarillo

For children learning Spanish there are also the following books by Joanne Leyland:

Spanish Colouring Book For Kids Ages 5-7

Learning your very first words in Spanish is fun with this fantastic colouring book! The following ten topics are covered in this book: toys, pets, transport, picnic, summer, zoo, fruit, countryside, town and vegetables.

Jack And The Spanish Dinosaur

With six fantastic stories. The Spanish dinosaur introduces / reinforces Spanish words within an English storyline. Vocabulary page at end of book. Ages 3 - 7

First Words In Spanish
Teacher's Resource Book   Ages 3 - 7

Learning Spanish is fun with the great games and activity sheets in this fantastic book. Topics include: pets, colours, transport, café, supermarket, hobbies, toys and Christmas.

Daniel And The Spanish Robot
Books 1, 2 & 3   Ages 3 - 7

In each book there are 2 fantastic stories. The Spanish robot introduces / reinforces Spanish words within an English storyline. At the end of the book is a Spanish vocabulary page.

Young Cool Kids Learn Spanish

A fun activity book for kids ages 5-7. The fun activities for practising Spanish include matching the words to pictures by drawing a line, circling the correct word, word searches and copying or writing just a few words per page. The book is full of Spanish words and images for these words that the children can colour as they look at the Spanish words. The topics in this book include Numbers 1-10, Pet animals, Essential Spanish words, Clothes, The garden, The farm, Colours and Ice creams.

For more information about learning Spanish and the great books by Joanne Leyland go to
https://funspanishforkids.com

Printed in Great Britain
by Amazon

24354535R00018